Rewrite this sentence, putting in the necessary punctuation.	1-5.	several times said elizabeth worriedly ive heard

Number between 0 and 5 ☐

_____

_____

_____

Complete these definitions.	6.	A topiarist enjoys cutting _____ ☐
	7.	A meteorologist studies _____ ☐
	8.	A horticulturist enjoys _____ ☐
	9.	A phillumenist collects _____ ☐
	10.	An oenologist is an expert on _____ ☐

Complete these statements, making NOUNS from the words in capitals.	11.	AVID means 'eager' and its noun is _____ ☐
	12.	SUITABLE means 'fitting' and its noun is _____ ☐
	13.	FRAGILE means 'delicate' and its noun is _____ ☐
	14.	INDOLENT means 'idle' and its noun is _____ ☐
	15.	EQUAL means 'the same' and its noun is _____ ☐

Complete these sentences using a word which expresses a likeness to other creatures, e.g. 'bovine' means <u>like a cow.</u>	16.	<u>like an eagle</u> He had an _____ nose. ☐
	17.	<u>like a cat</u> She moved with a _____ grace. ☐
	18.	<u>like a dog</u> He preferred _____ company to that of any human being. ☐
	19.	<u>like a pig</u> His _____ eating habits were disgusting. ☐
	20.	<u>like a wild beast</u> They attacked with _____ ferocity. ☐

Underline the odd one out in each line.	21.	blessed cursed sacred hallowed sanctified ☐
	22.	remuneration celery payment reward salary ☐
	23.	Aunt Sally Uncle George laughing-stock victim target ☐
	24.	trusting born yesterday gullible repudiating credulous ☐
	25.	sack loot pillage plunder donate ☐

Complete these proverbs.	26.	Rome was not _____ ☐
	27.	It's no use crying _____ ☐
	28.	There are none so deaf _____ ☐
	29.	Man proposes but _____ ☐
	30.	Dead men _____ ☐

MARK
✓ or ✗

The prefix 'super-' means 'above' or 'very'. Complete these sentences.

31. Magical or mystical is   super _ _ _ _ _ _ _ .

32. If you are disdainful or superior in manner, you are
super _ _ _ _ _ _ _ .

33. To be in charge is to   super _ _ _ _ .

34. A very large shop is a   super _ _ _ _ _ _ .

35. A high-ranking police officer is a   super _ _ _ _ _ _ _ _ _ .

Write each of these foreign phrases next to its correct meaning.

kismet, viva voce, nil desperandum, crème de la crème,
victor ludorum

36. an oral exam (live voice) _____

37. never say die, don't give up _____

38. fate _____

39. the very best _____

40. the winner of the games _____

In each sentence write an ADVERB made from the word in capitals.

41. CIVIL   Mohammed spoke _____ to me.

42. TERRIBLE   Jane was _____ upset when the dog died.

43. PRETTY   The little girl curtsied _____ .

44. UNCANNY   That voice sounds _____ familiar.

45. MIGHT   When he heard the news he was _____
afraid.

Difficult spellings. Put in the missing letters.

46. utterly stupid   r _ _ _ c _ _ _ _ _ _

47. a way of doing something   p _ _ c _ _ _ _ _ _ _

48. keeps off the rain   u _ _ _ _ _ _ _ _

49. easy to love   l _ _ _ _ _ _ _

50. has three stripes on his or her arm   s _ _ _ _ _ _ _ _

Write each of these words in its correct sentence.

adds, adze, air, heir, ere

51. " _____ morning comes," said the evil witch, "you
will turn into a frog."

52. Fresh _____ is good for us.

53. In the Middle Ages an _____ was often used to cut
and shape wood.

54. The _____ to the throne was a handsome prince.

55. What you have won _____ up to a tidy sum of money.

MARK
✓ or ✗

What unpleasant thing would be happening to you?	56.	If you were under the sword of Damocles you would have been in very great _____ .
	57.	If you were press-ganged you would be kidnapped and forced to join the _____ .
	58.	If you were incarcerated you would be put in _____ .
	59.	If you were on the rack you would be being _____ .
	60.	If you were guillotined your head would be _____ .

Write down antonyms of the words in capitals.	61.	Instead of sustaining a LOSS for the year the company made a huge _____ .
	62.	The SUCCESSOR to the throne wore the coronation regalia which his _____ had worn many years before.
	63.	There was a DEARTH of food before the rains came but now there is an _____ .
	64.	They feared that they might have to _____ building the estate, but a new investor enabled them to CONTINUE the project.
	65.	He expected the committee to give their ASSENT to his proposal but was surprised by their cries of _____ .

A simile compares one thing with another, e.g. Margaret runs like a hare. Use your imagination and write a really interesting simile to complete each of these sentences.	66.	The ogre roared like _____
	67.	The moon sailed across the sky like _____ _____
	68.	The steam locomotive emerged at great speed from the tunnel, like _____
	69.	The witch's voice was shrill, like _____ _____
	70.	The pastoral landscape before her was as _____ _____

In each of these sentences write a VERB made from the word in capitals.	71.	HORRIFYING I was _____ when I heard the dreadful news.
	72.	VERIFICATION Are you able to _____ your whereabouts on the night of the robbery?
	73.	TRANSACTION I have to _____ some business in town.
	74.	FALSIFICATION You may be prosecuted if you _____ your income tax return.
	75.	PUTREFACTION Meat will soon _____ if left for any length of time in a warm atmosphere.

MARK
✓ or ✗

Write each of these sentences out correctly.

76. This house is our's, not your's.

_____

77. The poor cats lost it's tail.

_____

78. Which of the car's is their's?

_____

79. Ones got to look after ones possession's.

_____

80. Im sure that jackets her's and not hi's.

_____

Briefly explain each of these words or phrases.

81. cross-examine _____

82. crossword _____

83. cross my heart _____

84. crossbow _____

85. cross-country _____

Write out the names of these counties in full.

86. Lincs. _____

87. Northants. _____

88. Oxon. _____

89. IOW _____

90. Salop. _____

Complete this information.

91. 'Mayhem' is a word meaning total _____ .

92. A pennant is a long, narrow _____ .

93. A Stradivarius is an old, valuable _____ .

94. The word 'stellar' refers to _____ .

95. A sobriquet or soubriquet is a _____ .

Write down these plurals.

96. A GOOSE is a domestic fowl and its plural is _____ .

97. A tailor's iron is called a GOOSE because of the shape of its handle. Its plural is _____ .

98. A place for keeping geese is a GOOSERY and its plural is

_____ .

99. A GOOSEBERRY is a fruit. Its plural is _____ .

100. A GOOSEFOOT is a plant of the beet family and its plural is

_____ .

MARK
✓ or ✗

Rewrite these sentences, putting in the necessary punctuation.

1. is my tea ready sam asked his mother
   _____ ☐

2. mother asked sam is my tea ready
   _____ ☐

3. sam asked his mother if his tea was ready
   _____ ☐

4. is my tea ready mother asked sam
   _____ ☐

5. im starving to death sam cried dolefully
   _____ ☐

Underline the odd one out in each line.

6. drastic   lenient   Draconian   extreme   severe ☐
7. build   raze   construct   erect   fabricate ☐
8. victuals   fare   rations   sustenance   flower ☐
9. yacht   junk   sloop   gallon   man-o'-war ☐
10. valet   Man Friday   factotum   butler   merchant ☐

Complete this information.

11. A vintner sells _____ . ☐
12. A dormer is a _____ . ☐
13. A cornucopia is a _____ of plenty, an abundant supply. ☐
14. Cordite is used to make _____ . ☐
15. The word paschal refers to _____ . ☐

In each sentence write a NOUN formed from the word in capitals.

16. GENIAL   Adam made us feel at ease by his warmth and
    _____ . ☐

17. EUPHORIC   Fay was filled with _____ when she won. ☐

18. CONVENE   The sales executives got together at their annual
    _____ . ☐

19. ABHOR   I look upon your dreadful crime with
    _____ . ☐

20. FERVENT   She began the task with _____ and
    enthusiasm. ☐

Rewrite these sentences, changing singulars to plurals.

21. I gave my loaf to my enemy's ally.
    _____ ☐

22. His ravenous ox devoured my potato crop.
    _____ ☐

23. She used her scissors to cut the sheep's wool.
    _____ ☐

MARK
✓ or ✗

Rewrite these sentences, changing singulars to plurals.	24.	The passer-by took the sharp knife from the child.
	25.	The dingo chased the kangaroo across the plateau.

In each sentence write the past participle of the word in capitals.

26. OVERDO — "The potatoes are mushy," Alice complained. "I must have _____ them."

27. REND — In his temper David had _____ the curtains asunder.

28. REWIND — Whilst somnambulating, Sita had _____ the clock.

29. REWRITE — The book had been _____ many times before it was considered suitable for publication.

30. SLIDE — Going through the oily patch on the road, the lorry had _____ into the ditch.

In each sentence write an ADJECTIVE formed from the word in capitals.

31. DEXTERITY — With a _____ flick of the wrist, Nigel manoeuvred the car round the hairpin bend.

32. ADDICT — Anything that is harmful and _____ should be avoided.

33. DISDAIN — With a _____ snort of contempt the rich man strutted past the indigent beggar.

34. LUCRE — Angela obtained a _____ job managing a shop.

35. ORIENT — In Burma they studied the _____ way of life.

These words are often-used contractions of longer words. Write down each word in full, e.g. photo_photograph.

36. auto _____
37. cello _____
38. gym _____
39. specs _____
40. prom _____

Complete these proverbs.

41. The Devil makes work _____
42. You cannot have your cake _____
43. Everything comes to _____
44. A fair exchange _____
45. What the eye does not see _____

Difficult spellings. Fill in the missing letters.

46. People waiting in a line are q _ _ _ _ _ _ _ .
47. Lines always the same distance apart are p _ _ _ _ _ _ _ _ .

MARK
✓ or ✗

48. We ate a meal from a basket which we had taken out into the countryside. We   p _ _ _ _ _ _ _ _ _ .

49. I love chocolate. The urge to eat it is   ir _ _ _ _ _ _ _ _ _ _ _ .

50. To confirm that something is so is to   co _ _ _ _ _ _ _ _ _ _ it.

Here are some unusual names for colours. Write down the colour of which each one is a shade.

51. Gamboge is a shade of _____ .

52. Ochre is a shade of _____ .

53. Amethyst is a shade of _____ .

54. Beryl is a shade of _____ .

55. Camel is a shade of _____ .

Next to each of these countries write its capital city and its currency from this list.

Helsinki, Krone, Sucre, Brasilia, Copenhagen, Cruzeiro, Markka, Canberra, Quito, Dollar

COUNTRY	CAPITAL	CURRENCY
56. Australia	_____	_____
57. Finland	_____	_____
58. Denmark	_____	_____
59. Brazil	_____	_____
60. Ecuador	_____	_____

Put each of these words into its correct sentence.

load, lode, lowed, grill, grille

61. The plumber removed the _____ to repair the heater.

62. The cattle _____ contentedly in the meadow at night.

63. _____ the wagon so that we can be off on our deliveries.

64. You must _____ the steak until it is tender.

65. A _____ is a deposit of valuable ore in rock.

Put each of these names into its correct sentence.

Judas, Shakespeare, Morpheus, Achilles, Echo

66. _____ was a nymph who loved Narcissus. He did not return her love, so she pined away until only her voice remained.

67. The little child lay in his cot, asleep in the arms of _____ .

68. A person who betrays his friends or country is often referred to as a _____ .

69. Someone's weak spot is his or her _____ heel.

70. _____ is known as the Bard of Avon.

Write one word to describe all on each line.

71. Superior Huron Victoria Bala Windermere _____

72. Brer Peter White Fiver Bugs _____

MARK
✓ or ✗

Write one word to describe all on each line.	73.	Times Telegraph Mail Express Mirror _____
	74.	Watson Who Jekyll Grace Foster _____
	75.	salt mustard vinegar pepper _____

Write down the meanings of these abbreviations.	76.	Messrs _____
	77.	JP _____
	78.	HMG _____
	79.	MBE _____
	80.	GP _____

Briefly explain these phrases.	81.	civil service _____
	82.	civil war _____
	83.	civil rights _____
	84.	civil list _____
	85.	civil law _____

Complete these analogies.	86.	Colosseum is to Rome as Leaning Tower is to _____ .
	87.	Freyja is to Friday as Woden is to _____ .
	88.	Scafell Pike is to England as _____ is to Scotland.
	89.	The Mayflower was to the _____ as the Santa Maria was to Christopher Columbus.
	90.	Harp is to Ireland as leek is to _____ .

Members of the orchestra.	91.	A person who plays the flute is a _____
	92.	A person who plays the violin is a _____
	93.	A person who plays the cello is a _____
	94.	A person who plays the timpani is a _____
	95.	A person who plays the piano is a _____

A spoonerism is the swapping of the initial sounds of words, e.g. You must leave by the *town drain*, instead of *down train*. Underline the words in which the sounds need to be transposed. Then write the correct words underneath.	96.	We searched every crook and nanny for the missing ring. _____
	97.	My favourite poets are Sheets and Kelley. _____
	98.	You have learned nothing for weeks and have tasted the whole worm. _____
	99.	The vicar told us that the Lord is a shoving leopard. _____
	100.	He has a half-warmed fish to go to Disneyland. _____

MARK
✓ or ✗

Rewrite this sentence, putting in all the necessary punctuation.	1-5.	dads hammers missing moaned sam so i cant fix those new planks on the shed for mrs goodwins mother

Number between 0 and 5
☐

Underline the odd one out in each line.	6.	snooze browse doze drowse nap	☐
	7.	high and mighty down-and-out condescending snooty toffee-nosed	☐
	8.	qualm anxiety regret apprehension misgiving	☐
	9.	jeer deride ridicule mock criticise	☐
	10.	wax dwindle abate decrease ebb wane	☐

Write down the antonyms of these words.	11.	maximum _____	☐
	12.	antonym _____	☐
	13.	Arctic _____	☐
	14.	politeness _____	☐
	15.	sophisticated _____	☐

Put each of these words into its correct sentence.		frees, freeze, frieze, jam, jamb	
	16.	It's unusual for water to _____ at this time of year.	☐
	17.	In the darkness he bumped into the door _____ .	☐
	18.	See how the bee _____ itself from the spider's web.	☐
	19.	With all that fruit, we shall be able to make a lot of _____ .	☐
	20.	The decorator pasted a pretty _____ along the top of the room walls.	☐

Write down the plurals of these words.	21.	that _____	☐
	22.	this _____	☐
	23.	me _____	☐
	24.	my _____	☐
	25.	its _____	☐

Complete these analogies.	26.	Nile is to longest river as _____ is to highest mountain.	☐
	27.	Thirty is to June as _____ is to August.	☐
	28.	_____ are to New Zealand as Aborigines are to Australia.	☐
	29.	Lister is to antiseptics as Jenner is to _____ .	☐
	30.	Sovereign is to one hundred as guinea is to _____ .	☐

MARK
✓ or ✗

Briefly describe these phrases.

31. powder horn _____
32. powder-monkey _____
33. powder-puff _____
34. powder-room _____
35. keep one's powder dry _____

Underline one word in each line which is closest in meaning to the word in capitals.

36. NEGLIGENCE   exhibition   hopelessness   carelessness   ruthlessness
37. QUANDARY   dilemma   quagmire   attribute   laundry   mystery
38. PYROMANIAC   lunatic   bigamist   madman   arsonist   sadist
39. RUBICUND   facetious   hilarious   ruddy   rotund   pallid
40. INANE   awkward   definite   sensible   senseless   dead

In each sentence write a NOUN formed from the word in capitals.

41. FESTIVE   The Christmas period is a time for great _____ .
42. CONTRAVENE   Any _____ of the rules will be punished.
43. ABSTAIN   Some people believe that total _____ from tobacco and alcohol is necessary for good health.
44. CONVALESCE   After her operation, Mary's _____ took many months.
45. DRAMATIC   The play was written by a well-known _____ .

Complete these sentences.

46. Plates, cups and saucers are all items of _____ .
47. Tropical fish are kept in an _____ .
48. A gymnast who performs on stage or in a circus is an _____ .
49. A large feather, sharpened with a penknife and once used for writing is known as a _____ .
50. An optical toy showing a constant variety of beautiful colours is called a   k_____ .

Supply the missing information.

51. If you are AMBIDEXTROUS you are able to write equally well with _____ .
52. A KIBBUTZ in Israel is a _____ .
53. A PROMONTORY is a piece of land which _____ _____ .

54. A SASSENACH is what a _____ person sometimes calls an _____ person.

55. A SCALENE triangle has sides of _____.

In each sentence write an ADJECTIVE formed from the word in capitals.

56. ENIGMA   When I asked what he had meant he looked at me with an _____ smile on his face.

57. NEUROSIS   Mother becomes quite _____ if I don't wash my hands thoroughly before eating.

58. EMPHASIS   ''You must never talk to strangers,'' said the teacher. ''On this matter I am absolutely _____.''

59. RHYTHM   The warriors danced to the _____ beat of the war-drums.

60. DOGMA   Mr Hughes is often overbearing and _____ , unwilling to consider anybody else's opinion.

The prefix 'hypo-' means 'under' or 'inadequate'. Complete these sentences.

61. A needle which is used to inject beneath the skin is known as a hypo _ _ _ _ _ _ needle.

62. A hypo _ _ _ _ _ was the Roman method of heating beneath the floor by hot air.

63. A person who always seems to imagine that he or she is ill or 'under the weather' is a hypo _ _ _ _ _ _ _ _ _ .

64. The side of a right-angled triangle opposite to the right angle is called the hypo _ _ _ _ _ _ .

65. Someone exposed to the cold and suffering from very low body temperature has hypo _ _ _ _ _ _ _ .

Work out these sums and write out the answers in words.

66. Add together a brace and a score. _____

67. Subtract a dozen from a gross. _____

68. Multiply a couple by a baker's dozen. _____

69. Add together a pair and a duck. _____

70. Add a decade, a century and a millennium and subtract a couple. _____

Complete these collective terms using the words given.

posse, host, covey, flock, flight

71. a _____ of grouse

72. a _____ of steps

73. a _____ of birds

74. a _____ of angels

75. a _____ of policemen

MARK
✓ or ✗

Complete each sentence with the comparative or superlative degree of the word in capitals.	76.	GOOD In today's hockey match, ours was the _____ team.
	77.	GOOD As all the runners set off I shouted, "May the _____ man win!"
	78.	SMALL Paul is the _____ of the two boys.
	79.	SMALL Nicola is the _____ child in the class.
	80.	GREEDY Wayne is the _____ person I have ever met.

Write down one word on each line which has both the meanings given.	81.	to give an image in a mirror _____ to meditate
	82.	a cooking utensil _____ a Greek god
	83.	to provide _____ the adverb from 'supple'
	84.	the front _____ a large covered wagon
	85.	to lean to one side _____ a catalogue

Difficult spellings. Fill in the missing letters.	86.	Something which passes the time is a p _ _ _ _ _ _ .
	87.	Someone who writes shorthand, types, answers the telephone, keeps records and works for a boss is a s _ _ _ _ _ _ _ _ _ .
	88.	Plays are performed in a t _ _ _ _ _ _ .
	89.	A word meaning 'completely' is w _ _ _ _ _ .
	90.	If you disagree with somebody you might have an a _ _ _ _ _ _ _ .

Members of the orchestra.	91.	A person who plays the oboe is an _____ .
	92.	A person who plays the organ is an _____ .
	93.	A person who plays the clarinet is a _____ .
	94.	A person who plays the trombone is a _____ .
	95.	A person who plays the piano to accompany a singer is called an _____ .

Join these pairs of sentences together. Your first word should be 'Having' and you should use a comma, e.g. Having seen the accident take place, he ran across the road to help.	96.	Mary lost the key to her door. She was unable to get in.
	97.	Mrs Jones did her shopping. She caught the bus home.
	98.	Siama mowed the lawn. She then planted some bulbs.
	99.	George read the question. He began to write.
	100.	The surveyors decided that the derelict building was unsafe. They ordered it to be demolished.

MARK
✓ or ✗

Write down the missing parts of speech on each line.

	NOUN	ADVERB	VERB	ADJECTIVE	
1.	_____	_____	SUFFICE	_____	☐
2.	COMPREHENSION	_____	_____	_____	☐
3.	_____	_____	RESOLVE	_____	☐
4.	_____	_____	IDLE	_____	☐
5.	_____	_____	_____	SYMPATHETIC	☐

Underline the odd one out in each line.

6. fireman   fire-bug   arsonist   pyromaniac   incendiary ☐
7. scribe   lector   amanuensis   writer   clerk ☐
8. genesis   beginning   inception   start   finale ☐
9. Hades   Heaven   nirvana   paradise   bliss ☐
10. shallow   deep   frivolous   puerile   superficial ☐

Briefly describe each of these phrases.

11. long shot _____ ☐
12. long leg _____ ☐
13. long odds _____ ☐
14. long-winded _____ ☐
15. long-drawn-out _____ ☐

Complete these analogies.

16. Overt is to _____ as open is to hidden. ☐
17. Greek is to Poseidon as Roman is to _____ . ☐
18. Harold was to Hastings as _____ was to Waterloo. ☐
19. Jeeves is to Wooster as batman is to _____ . ☐
20. Vulcan is to fire as Mars is to _____ . ☐

Underline one word on the right which belongs with the three on the left.

21. hansom, gig, trap | beautiful, buggy, dance, snare ☐
22. sliver, modicum, morsel | shred, sled, shed, sped ☐
23. referee, judge, umpire | captain, manager, player, arbitrator ☐
24. dumb, mute, silent | shut up, dad, mum, aunt ☐
25. absolute, total, complete | speak, state, utter, success ☐

Work out these anagrams from the clues given.

26. THE ICE CRASH   (two words – an animal which always grins)
_____ ☐
27. ITS NEWS   (one who saw it happen) _____ ☐
28. THE CLASSROOM   (he works there) _____ ☐
29. TARRY USE   (where riches are kept) _____ ☐
30. TAGGED   (a device) _____ ☐

MARK
✓ or ✗

The word 'monger' means 'dealer' or 'trader' (either good dealing or bad). Write either BAD or GOOD after each of these 'mongers'.

31. ironmonger _____ ☐

32. fellmonger _____ ☐

33. scandalmonger _____ ☐

34. costermonger _____ ☐

35. scaremonger _____ ☐

Write down one word which describes all in each line.

36. sideboard ottoman tallboy chesterfield _____ ☐

37. neon ozone propane xenon _____ ☐

38. holt earth hive rookery _____ ☐

39. gin whisky rum vodka _____ ☐

40. whippet chow pug beagle _____ ☐

Write down each of these Latin phrases next to its correct meaning.

in loco parentis, cave, sub rosa, inter alia, curriculum vitae

41. secretly _____ ☐

42. among other things _____ ☐

43. in the place of a parent _____ ☐

44. Watch out! _____ ☐

45. a list of one's jobs and achievements _____ ☐

Underline the malapropism in each sentence and write the correct word beneath it.

46. The information was given to me by a neutral friend.
_____ ☐

47. The explorer set off on a dangerous exposition into the dense jungle.
_____ ☐

48. The problem was intimate and very difficult to solve.
_____ ☐

49. I am looking forward to my summer vocation.
_____ ☐

50. A person who always expects the worst to happen is a pharmacist.
_____ ☐

Rewrite this sentence, putting in the necessary punctuation.

51-55. dr clarks nephew will be here at two oclock tomorrow promised henrys mother and ill be glad to see him

_____

_____

_____
☐

MARK
✓ or ✗

In each line underline a word most nearly opposite to the one in capitals.		
56.	STARBOARD	prow bow port dock stern anchor
57.	FEW	lot score heaps many plenty millions
58.	INHALE	breathe breath rain pour exhale sniff
59.	SINGLE	couple return backward one only lots
60.	FORE	eight number aft front warning against

Complete these definitions.

61. A tabloid is a _____ .

62. A centaur was _____ .

63. A fjord is a narrow _____ .

64. Another word for medley is _____ .

65. A cutlass was a _____ .

Plurals. Complete the following.

66. A GRIZZLY is a large bear living in the Rocky Mountains of Canada and the United States. Its plural is _____ .

67. The plural of LARVA is _____ .

68. The plural of FUNGUS is either

_____ or _____ .

69. The word LAVATORY really means a place for washing. The plural is _____ .

70. A GYPSY (or gipsy) is a Romany or traveller and the plural is

_____ (or _____).

Which animals are sometimes known by these names?

71. Bruin _____

72. Reynard _____

73. Leo _____

74. Brock _____

75. Felix _____

Complete these phrases using the sounds given.

skirl,   hiss,   crack,   slam,   jingle

76. the _____ of a door

77. the _____ of steam

78. the _____ of a rifle

79. the _____ of coins

80. the _____ of the bagpipes

MARK
✓ or ✗

More prefixes. Fill in the missing letters.

81. The prefix 'haemo-' means blood. A sufferer from haemo _ _ _ _ _ bleeds too much even after a very slight injury. ☐

82. The prefix 'pseudo-' means false, so a false name is a pseudo _ _ _ . ☐

83. The prefix 'archae-' means ancient. The study of our past by digging for clues is archae _ _ _ _ _ . ☐

84. The prefix 'auto-' means self, so a vehicle which moves itself is an auto _ _ _ _ _ _ . ☐

85. The prefix 'ultra-' means beyond. Noise which is beyond normal human hearing is called ultra _ _ _ _ _ . ☐

Put each of these words into its correct sentence.

vain, vein, vane, surge, serge

86. The crowd began to _____ forward as the gates opened. ☐

87. Caroline waited in _____ for the bus to come. ☐

88. The blood oozed from the cut _____ . ☐

89. Albert's working trousers were made of green _____ . ☐

90. The weather _____ was blown from the roof in the storm. ☐

Here are some more unusual names for colours. Write down the colour of which each one is a shade.

91. Oxford is a shade of _____ . ☐

92. Amber is a shade of _____ . ☐

93. Saffron is a shade of _____ . ☐

94. Sage is a shade of _____ . ☐

95. Magenta is a shade of _____ . ☐

Difficult spellings. Fill in the missing letters.

96. If you can manage to do something, it is m _ _ _ _ _ _ _ _ _ . ☐

97. If you commit a crime, it has been c _ _ _ _ _ _ _ _ . ☐

98. Twenty-two plus twenty equals f _ _ _ _ - _ _ _ . ☐

99. A group of people working together is an a _ _ _ _ _ _ t _ _ _ . ☐

100. That's funny, the adjective from humour is h _ _ _ _ _ _ _ . ☐

MARK
✓ or ✗

Underline the word in each line which is closest in meaning to the word in capitals.

1. RAIMENT　　sunshine　glory　poverty　clothing　wealth ☐

2. VALOROUS　　bravery　cowardice　brave　hero　bravely ☐

3. PROFICIENT　incompetent　friendly　awful　serious　competent ☐

4. JUBILANT　　euphoric　jubilee　angry　impartial　fierce ☐

5. CONVIVIAL　unfriendly　inquisitive　fair　jovial　peaceful ☐

In each sentence write a NOUN formed from the word in capitals.

6. SUDDEN　　The _____ of the lion's attack surprised the visitors to the safari park. ☐

7. EMERGE　　The sudden _____ of the potholer from the cave surprised his friends. ☐

8. MAGNIFICENT　The _____ of the scenery brought many tourists to the area. ☐

9. ANTIQUE　　The vase was obviously of great _____ . ☐

10. PECULIAR　　The duck-billed platypus has many _____ . ☐

Rewrite these sentences correctly.

11. The yoke of an egg are white.

_____ ☐

12. The whole library of books were destroyed by fire.

_____ ☐

13. Which of the two reds is nearest the pocket?

_____ ☐

14. Whose coming with Jim and I to the party?

_____ ☐

15. The soldiers attacked the gorilla camp in order to free their kernel who had been held as an ostrich for more than a weak.

_____

_____ ☐

Who might be the 'opposite' of each of these people?

16. batsman _____ ☐

17. author _____ ☐

18. finder _____ ☐

19. donor _____ ☐

20. waiter _____ ☐

Complete these definitions.

21. A PLACEBO is a _____ given to a patient just to keep him or her happy but which doesn't actually do anything. ☐

22. An ARCHIPELAGO is a large group of _____ . ☐

MARK
✓ or ✗

Complete these definitions.	23.	On a painting a _____ is the ring round the head of a saint or holy person.
	24.	PROBOSCIS is another name for your _____ .
	25.	SEMAPHORE is the use of flags to _____ .

In each sentence write the plural of the word in capitals.	26.	A GRAFFITO is a writing or scribbling on a wall and its plural is _____ .
	27.	The LIBRETTO is the book of words to an opera and its plural is either _____ or _____ .
	28.	An ITINERARY is the route of a journey and its plural is _____ .
	29.	A DISCREPANCY is a conflict or difference between facts and its plural is _____ .
	30.	The plural of MINE can be either _____ or _____ .

Unscramble these anagrams using the clues given.	31.	MICE END UP	(great cheek) _____
	32.	TO PLACE	(an animal) _____
	33.	ALIAS NAT	(a dog) _____
	34.	A STRAIN	(skilled worker) _____
	35.	RUN EVEN	(to worry) _____

Write down the meanings of these '-ologies'.	36.	Palaeontology is the study of _____ .
	37.	Ornithology is the study of _____ .
	38.	Ichthyology is the study of _____ .
	39.	Hydrology is the study of _____ .
	40.	Dermatology is the study of _____ .

Here are some more unusual names for colours. Write down the colour of which each one is a shade.	41.	puce _____
	42.	cerise _____
	43.	jasmine _____
	44.	hazel _____
	45.	ebony _____

Briefly describe each of these words or phrases.	46.	jack-in-office _____
	47.	jack-o'-lantern _____
	48.	jackpot _____
	49.	Jack Russell _____
	50.	steeplejack _____

Rewrite these sentences as indirect (or reported) speech.	51.	"Mary," asked Yasmin, "do you think I might borrow your pen?" _____ ☐
	52.	"What are you doing?" the security guard asked me in a gruff voice. _____ ☐
	53.	"Halt!" the gamekeeper shouted at the poacher. "Or I'll set the dogs on you." _____ _____ ☐
	54.	"Becky," her mother said, "do you think I'm made of money?" _____ ☐
	55.	"Please come in," a neighbour said to me, "and make yourself at home." _____ ☐

Write one word on each line which has both the meanings given.	56.	a monk's hood	_____	the cover for a chimney ☐
	57.	not stiff	_____	to walk, dragging the leg ☐
	58.	to cleanse	_____	waves caused by a passing ship ☐
	59.	mould	_____	to be obliged to ☐
	60.	to harass, destroy or plunder	_____	a Prince's name ☐

Write down the name of an animal as the answer to each of these definitions, e.g. to imitate or mimic is to <u>ape</u>.	61.	To follow people you _____ them. ☐
	62.	If you outwit people you _____ them. ☐
	63.	When you eat greedily you _____ your food. ☐
	64.	If you pester people you _____ them. ☐
	65.	To force or push hard is to _____ . ☐

In each sentence write an ADJECTIVE formed from the word in capitals.	66.	CHIVALRY — The _____ young man held open the door for the young woman to enter the room. ☐
	67.	ORGAN — _____ substances soon decompose in the soil. ☐
	68.	PRETEND — The _____ newcomer imagined he would soon be capable of taking over the boss's job. ☐
	69.	VITUPERATE — The cyclist's _____ language caused the car driver great embarrassment. ☐
	70.	GRAPH — The speaker gave a _____ account of his trip up the River Amazon. ☐

Difficult spellings. Fill in the missing letters.	71.	If you agree to something then you are a _ _ _ _ _ _ _ _ _ _ to it. ☐
	72.	If you are brave you are c _ _ _ _ _ _ _ _ _ . ☐
	73.	When there is far too much of something, the amount is said to be e _ _ _ _ _ _ _ _ . ☐

MARK
✓ or ✗

Difficult spellings. Fill in the missing letters.	74.	Someone violent and spiteful is said to be v _ _ _ _ _ _ .
	75.	A word which means complete, entire, out and out is t _ _ _ _ _ _ h.
Put each of these words into its correct sentence.		wear, ware, way, weigh, whey
	76.	I asked the greengrocer to _____ the potatoes.
	77.	The watery part of milk, separated from the curd, is _____ .
	78.	There is no right of _____ through that field, I'm afraid.
	79.	What are you going to _____ at the party tonight?
	80.	Anything for sale or an article of fine workmanship, such as a piece of Wedgwood pottery, is a _____ . Such things are often stored, before they are sold, in a _____ house.
Underline the VERBS in each line. There may be more than one.	81.	arrive kitchen they peace welcome depart
	82.	green deer person hope hop biscuit
	83.	we take ugly raindrop token omnibus
	84.	rays raise raze ruse rues rise
	85.	box shape signal brush comb holiday
Underline the correct word in the brackets.	86.	A person who guides a ship into port is a (pirate, pilot, Pilate).
	87.	The passenger seat on a motorcycle is the (pillory, pillow, pillion).
	88.	The dried kernel of the coconut is called (copper, copse, copra).
	89.	Confectionery made of a sweet paste and chopped almonds is called (nought, nougat, nugget).
	90.	A worker in metals is called a (smith, turner, gaffer).
In the brackets write one word which can come before all of the others in the line.		*Example* (air) man mail force port rifle
	91.	( ) martial house jester room order
	92.	( ) bed brain weight duster edge
	93.	( ) clamp barrow chair wright house
	94.	( ) lift jump slope run stick
	95.	( ) chocolate song sailing clothes flour
Underline the odd one out in each line.	96.	haulier sawyer farrier draper felon
	97.	venison meat veal beef pork lamb
	98.	levity ire mirth gaiety glee hilarity
	99.	furlough leave vacation departure holiday
	100.	nick half-inch swipe donate snitch lift

MARK
✓ or ✗

Write one word on each line which has both the meanings given.

1. not fat _____ to incline ☐

2. a tunnelling animal _____ a blemish on the skin ☐

3. to prod with the finger _____ a pocket or bag ☐

4. to bend the body forward _____ a container for holy water ☐

5. an old word meaning 'alive' _____ nimble, swift, lively ☐

Rewrite this sentence, putting in the necessary punctuation.

6-10. his excellency the count of boravia madam announced jenkins the butler in a sepulchral voice

_____

_____

_____

Number between 0 and 5 ☐

The prefix 'contra-' or 'contre-' means 'against'. Complete these sentences.

11. If you argue against somebody you contra _ _ _ _ him or her. ☐

12. A system for directing traffic in the wrong carriageway against the normal flow is called a contra _ _ _ _ . ☐

13. A hitch or something happening at the wrong time is a contre _ _ _ _ _ . ☐

14. To act against a law or rule is to contra _ _ _ _ it. ☐

15. Goods smuggled into a country against the law are called contra _ _ _ _ . ☐

In each sentence form an ADJECTIVE from the word in capitals.

16. REPULSION Rachel thinks smoking is a _____ habit. ☐

17. MUTINY The _____ sailors were locked up in the brig. ☐

18. REPTILE The thief gave a _____ smile as he drove away in the stolen car. ☐

19. SYMMETRY A square is a _____ shape. ☐

20. ASYMMETRY A scalene triangle is an _____ shape. ☐

Rewrite these phrases, putting in the necessary apostrophes.

21. Arthurs fathers friend _____ ☐

22. the fleets manoeuvres _____ ☐

23. Mary Poppins umbrella _____ ✓

24. Davy Joness locker _____ ☐

25. the gateaus taste _____ ☐

MARK
✓ or ✗

In each sentence write the past participle of the word in capitals.

26. SLING The armoured car had been _____ beneath the helicopter.

27. SLINK The tiger had _____ away into the undergrowth.

28. SMITE I think Bob's in love. He's really been _____ .

29. SPIT The llama that had _____ at the visitors was called Larry.

30. UNBIND At the hospital Carol's wound had been _____ .

Complete these definitions.

31. A busker is a wandering _____ .

32. A census is a _____ of all the people.

33. A parapet is a low _____ overlooking a steep drop.

34. A tandem is a _____ for _____ people.

35. A bung is the stopper of a _____ in a _____ .

In the brackets write one word which can come before all of the other words in the line.

36. (_____) parking jockey harrow drive brake

37. (_____) guard smith board currant mail

38. (_____) water gauge bow drop fall

39. (_____) father piano total opera stand

40. (_____) handle power Friday hole hunt

Write each of these words in its correct sentence.

populous, populace, precede, proceed, persecute

41. The mayor will _____ the councillors in the procession.

42. In the 1930s the Nazis in Germany began to _____ the Jews.

43. With all the new houses being built, this village is fast becoming a _____ place.

44. We are now ready to _____ with the sale of the house.

45. The _____ was asked to vote for a new government.

Write in words the number of the century in which each of these events took place, e.g. thirteenth, sixth, etc.

46. the century in which we now live _____

47. the Battle of Hastings in 1066 _____

48. the Roman invasion of Britain in AD 43 _____

49. the reign of Henry VIII from 1509 to 1547 _____

50. the Viking invasions of England, 850-871 _____

MARK
✓ or ✗

Underline the word on the right which belongs with the three on the left.	51.	Genesis, Exodus, Leviticus	Writings, Numbers, Books, Figures	☐
	52.	Sahara, Great Sandy, Negev	Pacific, Nile, Hull, Gobi	☐
	53.	Holloway, Dartmoor, Pentonville	Armley, Solihull, Walsall	☐
	54.	Vesuvius, Stromboli, Krakatoa	Etna, Mont Blanc, Everest, Ayers Rock	☐
	55.	Anne, Charlotte, Emily	Richard, Branwell, Austin, Herbert	☐

Work out these anagrams from the clues given.	56.	I SORE US (not cheerful or funny)	_____	☐
	57.	PREEN CART (works with wood)	_____	☐
	58.	CAVERN (cowardly)	_____	☐
	59.	CAN I DIET (to point out)	_____	☐
	60.	RAM DAN IN (a Chinese official)	_____	☐

Underline the odd one out in each line.	61.	petunia begonia freesia alopecia fuchsia	☐
	62.	sphere roundabout football cuboid disc	☐
	63.	amiable charming venomous winsome genial	☐
	64.	professional amateur novice probationer trainee	☐
	65.	camouflage reveal disguise conceal screen	☐

In each sentence form a NOUN from the word in capitals.	66.	MIGRATE Each autumn the birds begin their annual _____ .	☐
	67.	EXPRESS Her novel is an _____ of her beliefs.	☐
	68.	PERUSE After careful _____ of the document, Kevin signed it.	☐
	69.	INTEND It is their _____ to retire to Spain.	☐
	70.	RECESS During the _____ many people are out of work.	☐

Define these '-ologies'.	71.	Ophthalmology is the study of _____	☐
	72.	Zoology is the study of _____	☐
	73.	Cardiology is the study of _____	☐
	74.	Anthropology is the study of _____	☐
	75.	Psychology is the study of _____	☐

Here are some more unusual names for colours. Write down the colour of which each one is a shade.	76.	Cambridge _____	☐
	77.	pillar-box _____	☐
	78.	milk- _____	☐
	79.	khaki _____	☐
	80.	plum _____	☐

MARK
✓ or ✗

Write down the names of these counties in full.	81.	Middx. _____
	82.	Derbys. _____
	83.	Wilts. _____
	84.	Bucks. _____
	85.	W. Yorks. _____

Briefly describe these phrases.	86.	full toss _____
	87.	full nelson _____
	88.	full of oneself _____
	89.	fully-fledged _____
	90.	full moon _____

Fill in the missing antonyms.

91. CONCAVE describes something curving inwards. Something curving outwards is _____ .

92. PESSIMISM is a depressing and miserable view of life. A confident and hopeful view of life is called _____ .

93. One is at one's NADIR at the lowest point of one's fortunes or happiness. The highest point is one's _____ .

94. An IMMIGRANT is someone who comes into a country to live and an _____ is one who leaves the country to go and live somewhere else.

95. Lines of LATITUDE run from west to east on a map. Lines of _____ run from north to south.

Some more prefixes. Complete these definitions.

96. 'Syn-' is a prefix meaning 'together'. Before starting our walk, we should   syn _ _ _ _ _ _ _ _   our watches to ensure they are all showing the same time.

97. 'Uni-' is a prefix meaning 'one'. When we all sing together as one person, we sing in   uni _ _ _ .

98. 'Equi-' is a prefix meaning 'equal'. In March and September there is a spring and autumn   equi _ _ _   when the night is equal in length to the day.

99. 'Hemi-' is a prefix meaning 'half'. Britain is situated in the northern   hemi _ _ _ _ _ _   on the Earth's surface.

100. 'Manu-' is a prefix meaning 'by hand'. A piece of paper with handwriting on it is a   manu _ _ _ _ _ _ .

MARK
✓ or ✗

In the brackets write one word which can come before all of the other words in the line.	1. ( ) float tooth shake maid chocolate	☐
	2. ( ) boy castle bank paper stone	☐
	3. ( ) craft hunt doctor hazel	☐
	4. ( ) light dream break return trip	☐
	5. ( ) ware shoulder pressed up labour	☐

A simile compares one thing with another, e.g. the poor boy was as pale as death. Use your imagination and write an interesting simile to complete each of these sentences.

6. The snow fell silently, as _____ ☐

7. The mountains towered above us, like _____

_____ ☐

8. The children followed the Pied Piper, as _____

_____ ☐

9. Thunder rumbled and the sky became dark, like _____

_____ ☐

10. Terry laughed, laughed fit to burst, like _____ ☐

Write in words the number of the century in which each of these events took place.

11. the reign of Richard II _____ ☐

12. the year Elizabeth I died _____ ☐

13. the Great Plague and Fire of London _____ ☐

14. the year Queen Victoria died _____ ☐

15. the English Civil War _____ ☐

Underline the word in each line which is closest in meaning to the word in capitals.

16. DUMBFOUNDED   keen interested astonished demented ☐

17. PERTURB   blossom disturb founder pervade ☐

18. SABOTAGE   damage gardening penmanship assistance ☐

19. QUAIL   fight believe demand flinch ☐

20. NONDESCRIPT   clever stupid not distinctive empty ☐

Complete the definitions of these studies.

21. Theology is the study of _____ ☐

22. Geology is the study of _____ ☐

23. Etymology is the study of _____ ☐

24. Gerontology is the study of _____ ☐

25. Paediatrics is the treatment of children's _____ ☐

Write down what these abbreviations stand for.

26. UHT _____ ☐

27. Bros. _____ ☐

28. RC _____ ☐

MARK
✓ or ✗

Write down what these abbreviations stand for.	29.	QPM _____
	30.	UFO _____

The prefix 'bi-' means 'two'. Complete these sentences.	31.	Something that happens twice a year is a bi _ _ _ _ _ _ event.
	32.	A vehicle with two wheels is a bi _ _ _ _ _ .
	33.	Someone able to speak two languages is bi _ _ _ _ _ _ _ .
	34.	Spectacles enabling you to see both far and near are described as bi _ _ _ _ _ .
	35.	Having two wives at once is called bi _ _ _ _ .

Complete these definitions.	36.	If you <u>genuflect</u> you are showing _____ to somebody.
	37.	A <u>pillory</u> was a frame for locking in the head and the hands of a _____ .
	38.	<u>Pince-nez</u> are glasses which clip to the _____ .
	39.	A <u>palisade</u> is a _____ of sharpened stakes.
	40.	An <u>epistle</u> is another word for a _____ .

Different languages. Fill in the missing words.	41.	The language spoken by the people of Egypt is _____ .
	42.	The main language spoken in Great Britain is _____ .
	43.	People in New Zealand speak _____ .
	44.	The people in Holland speak _____ .
	45.	The language spoken by the people of Denmark is _____ .

Rewrite these sentences in the past tense.	46.	I bear Robert no ill-will for the problem that arises. _____
	47.	I am awakened each morning by the dawn chorus which begins early. _____ _____
	48.	She blows her whistle as the game draws to a close. _____
	49.	Tasmin eats and drinks and then lies down. _____
	50.	The vandals run and tear down anything they choose. _____

MARK
✓ or ✗

Underline all the ADJECTIVES in these sentences.

51. Both players scored forty points. ☐

52. The second time the black dog appeared, I ran. ☐

53. Several interesting features appeared in the new magazine. ☐

54. "I don't believe either story," said Richard. "They're both stupid." ☐

55. Many may apply for the exciting job but few will be chosen. ☐

Join these pairs of sentences together. Start each new sentence with the word 'As' and use a comma.

56. Phillip was crossing the road. He saw Anne enter the shop.

_____ ☐

57. Mrs Briggs was reading. She heard the telephone ring.

_____ ☐

58. William climbed over the stile. The bull saw him.

_____ ☐

59. The burglar crept into the house. He tripped over the cat.

_____ ☐

60. Felix the cat slept soundly. The burglar tripped over him.

_____ ☐

In each sentence write the person formed from the word in capitals.

61. ADDRESS   The _____ returned the letter to the sender. ☐

62. EMPLOY   Liz is a good _____ and very rarely absent from work. ☐

63. TRAIN   Steve is a management _____ at our local supermarket. ☐

64. DEVOTION   A _____ of classical music will love Beethoven's symphonies. ☐

65. REFUGE   Karl is a _____ from eastern Europe. ☐

Put each of these words into its correct sentence.

hair,   hare,   heir,   human,   humane

66. The _____ to the throne is a tiny baby. ☐

67. I think it would be more _____ to have the injured animal destroyed. ☐

68. In one of Aesop's fables the _____ was beaten by the tortoise in a race. ☐

69. Many men lose much of their _____ by middle age. ☐

70. The creature, whatever it was, was certainly not _____ . ☐

Difficult spellings. Fill in the missing letters.

71. If you are being chased, then the person following you is your

p _ _ _ _ _ _ . ☐

72. The noun from repeat is   r _ _ _ _ _ _ _ _ _ . ☐

MARK
✓ or ✗

Difficult spellings. Fill in the missing letters.

73. When they die, people may be buried in a   c _ _ _ _ _ _ _ . ☐

74. A floating guide or warning in the sea is a   b _ _ _ . ☐

75. If you keep on asking for something, you are

i _ _ _ _ _ _ _ _ . ☐

Arrange these words alphabetically by writing the figures 1-5 inside the brackets.

76. Mary ( )   Mavis ( )   Maureen ( )   Millicent ( )   Miranda ( ) ☐

77. Murdoch ( )   Morgan ( )   Mark ( )   Matthew ( )   Melvin ( ) ☐

78. O'Dwyer ( )   Oliver ( )   O'Brien ( )   O'Reilly ( )   Odell ( ) ☐

79. Macbride ( )   McEnroe ( )   Macdonald ( )   Macpherson ( ) McCormack ( ) ☐

80. threshold ( )   three ( )   threat ( )   through ( )   throng ( ) ☐

These are the first lines of some well-known poems. At the end of each line write the name of the poet.

81. Old Meg she was a Gipsy _____ ☐

82. This is the Night Mail crossing the Border _____ ☐

83. 'Twas brillig and the slithy toves _____ ☐

84. The wind was a torrent of darkness among the gusty trees

_____ ☐

85. "Is there anybody there?" said the Traveller, _____ ☐

Underline the correct word in the brackets.

86. When I am sixty-five I will be (illegible, eligible) for a pension. ☐

87. The (forth, fourth) of July is Independence Day in America. ☐

88. A hiccup is caused by the involuntary contraction of the (diagram, diaphragm). ☐

89. Dick Turpin was a (notorious, eminent, illustrious) highwayman. ☐

90. It is illegal to do anything (prescribed, proscribed) by the law. ☐

Briefly define these words or phrases.

91. get it in the neck _____ ☐

92. neck and neck _____ ☐

93. bottleneck _____ ☐

94. break your neck _____ ☐

95. stick your neck out _____ ☐

Write the antonyms of these words, using or changing a prefix.

96. mortal _____ ☐

97. tolerable _____ ☐

98. introvert _____ ☐

99. reverent _____ ☐

100. necessary _____ ☐

MARK
✓ or ✗

In the brackets write one word which can come before all of the other words in the line.	1. ( ) speed ranking priest seas powered	☐
	2. ( ) dive bleed bag cone to-tail	☐
	3. ( ) collar watch house paddle tired	☐
	4. ( ) break failure felt string throb	☐
	5. ( ) down out on about kneed	☐

The prefix 'bio-' means 'life' or 'living things'. Complete these sentences.	6. The story of someone's life is called a bio _ _ _ _ _ _ _ .	☐
	7. The person who writes that story is a bio _ _ _ _ _ _ _ .	☐
	8. The science of living things is called bio _ _ _ _ .	☐
	9. A person who studies this science is a bio _ _ _ _ _ _ .	☐
	10. The removal of tissue from a living body for examination under a microscope is called a bio _ _ _ .	☐

Complete these definitions.	11. PLEBEIAN is a word meaning 'to do with _____ _____ '.	☐
	12. A MONARCH is crowned at his or her _____ ceremony.	☐
	13. A GNOMON is the arm of a _____ which casts a _____ .	☐
	14. A HEDONIST lives only for _____ .	☐
	15. A PLUMB is a lead weight on a line used to make sure that walls etc. are _____ .	☐

Write down the ADJECTIVES made from these proper nouns.	16.	PERU a _____ Indian	☐
	17.	BRITAIN the _____ economy	☐
	18.	PORTUGAL a _____ man-of-war (a jellyfish)	☐
	19.	NORWAY the _____ fjords (or fiords)	☐
	20.	FINLAND the _____ lakes	☐

In each of these sentences write a VERB formed from the word in capital letters.	21.	LIAISON The headteacher and the staff will have to _____ with one another to make sure everyone understands the new scheme.	☐
	22.	DISTILLERY It is illegal to _____ one's own whisky.	☐
	23.	VILIFICATION The sworn enemies used to _____ one another at every opportunity.	☐
	24.	FORTIFICATION In order to withstand the flood, it will be necessary to _____ the dam.	☐
	25.	RECTIFICATION I was told to _____ my mistakes before handing in my work.	☐

MARK
✓ or ✗

Write down the meaning of each abbreviation.	26.	VHF _____	☐
	27.	a.s.a.p. _____	☐
	28.	c.w.o. _____	☐
	29.	DPP _____	☐
	30.	OBE _____	☐

In each line underline the word which is closest in meaning to the word in capitals.	31.	HECKLE	hiccup freckle hackle haggle barrack	☐
	32.	FLEET	fast warship seaside gather newspaper	☐
	33.	CRINGE	haircut sprint blister bully cower	☐
	34.	WAGER	tail better gamble salary earner	☐
	35.	SURVEILLANCE	weapon surliness wimple trousseau observation	☐

Rewrite this sentence, putting in the necessary punctuation.	36-40.	charles dickens wrote many books mrs evans said but my personal favourite is a tale of two cities
		_____
		_____
		_____

Number between 0 and 5

☐

Work out these anagrams, using the clues given.	41.	CAPE GUNNER	(great dislike)	_____	☐
	42.	IS OUR GIRLIE	(ungodly)	_____	☐
	43.	NAME ONE	(flower)	_____	☐
	44.	MAN DATA	(not yielding)	_____	☐
	45.	QUARTO E	(around the world)	_____	☐

Put each of these words into its correct sentence.		immunity, impunity, allusion, delusion, illusion	
	46.	The savage dog had no fear of the farmer and attacked the flock of sheep with _____ .	☐
	47.	Sandra received a course of injections to gain _____ from certain tropical diseases.	☐
	48.	The new colour scheme gives the _____ of warmth and cosiness to the room.	☐
	49.	From the boss's _____ to my work, I gathered that I was in danger of losing my job.	☐
	50.	"You are suffering," I was told, "from the _____ that you are capable of doing the job, when in fact you're inept."	☐

Underline the NOUNS in each sentence.	51.	The quick brown fox jumped over the lazy goose.	☐
	52.	Whenever Midas touched an object, it turned to gold.	☐

MARK
✓ or ✗

53. Icarus flew too high in the sky and the wax on his wings melted. ☐

54. He fell to his death in the sea below. ☐

55. I'm not letting any Tom, Dick or Harry play with my football. ☐

Fill the gap in each sentence with one of these colours.	yellow, black, green, purple, blue	
	56. The little girl's hands and face were _____ with cold.	☐
	57. The old gentleman was _____ with rage when he saw the damage.	☐
	58. That coward has a _____ streak down his back.	☐
	59. Alison's exploits made her the _____ sheep of the family.	☐
	60. Jealousy, the _____ -eyed monster, caused them to separate.	☐

Briefly describe these words or phrases.	61. firearm _____	☐
	62. lay down one's arms _____	☐
	63. up in arms _____	☐
	64. coat of arms _____	☐
	65. armour _____	☐

The suffix '-less' means 'without'. Complete these sentences.	66. The teenager with nowhere to live was _ _ _ _ less.	☐
	67. I knew that my chances of success were _ _ _ _ less.	☐
	68. A knight should have courage and be _ _ _ _ less in battle.	☐
	69. _ _ _ _ less people seldom think of themselves.	☐
	70. That was a s _ _ _ _ less and pointless thing to do.	☐

Dwellings. Write down the creatures which live in these abodes.	71. vespiary _____	☐
	72. formicary _____	☐
	73. apiary _____	☐
	74. aviary _____	☐
	75. drey _____	☐

Underline the odd one out in each line.	76. Pleistocene Pliocene Plasticine Eocene Palaeocene	☐
	77. merciless harmless pitiless ruthless cruel	☐
	78. civil genteel courteous refined boorish	☐
	79. rhapsody nocturne serenade melodrama barcarole	☐
	80. marquis earl lord sir duke	☐

MARK
✓ or ✗

Use a form of the words 'lie' or 'lay' in each of these sentences.

81. He was _____ down on the floor. ☐

82. The rubbish had _____ there for weeks. ☐

83. My sister has _____ the table. ☐

84. Which hen has _____ the most eggs? ☐

85. They _____ down the injured boy very gently. ☐

Rewrite these sentences, changing to direct speech.

86. The new girl in the class said her name was Clare.
_____ ☐

87. The tourist asked me the way to the park.
_____ ☐

88. Sheila asked the tramp if he would like a cup of tea.
_____ ☐

89. John was told by the teacher that his work was disgraceful.
_____ ☐

90. Sarah asked her mother for some more pudding.
_____ ☐

Write down the antonyms of these words.

91. advance _____ ☐

92. tighten _____ ☐

93. fictional _____ ☐

94. roughness _____ ☐

95. madness _____ ☐

Malapropisms are words wrongly used instead of the proper ones. Rewrite these sentences correctly.

96. The milk was corrected and taken to the diary.
_____ ☐

97. A wooden petition separated the two areas.
_____ ☐

98. The blow to his temple caused him to suffer from discussion.
_____ ☐

99. The prodigious son wasted his money and then asked for patronal
forgiveness. _____
_____ ☐

100. "You're such an idiom," Mrs Moore said crossly to her scouse.
_____ ☐

MARK
✓ or ✗

In the brackets write one word which can come before all of the other words in the line.	1. ( )	path paint memorial horse monger
	2. ( )	dressing box ledge frame shopping
	3. ( )	pelt stop speed moon length
	4. ( )	place ball power side alarm
	5. ( )	manners spoon ware tennis mat

Write in words the number of the century in which these events happened.

6. the First World War _____

7. the reign of Charles II _____

8. St Augustine's arrival in England _____

9. the first voyage of Columbus to the West Indies _____

10. the American Declaration of Independence _____

In each sentence write an ADJECTIVE formed from the word in capitals.

11. CHANGE   The weather at this time of year is very

_____ .

12. KNOWLEDGE   The guide was a _____ man and told us many interesting facts about the ruined abbey.

13. NOTICE   The improvement in his behaviour is very

_____ .

14. MARRIAGE   When the princess reached _____ age, many suitors vied for her attention.

15. MANAGE   In winter the journey over the pass is very difficult and barely _____ .

The prefix 'trans-' means 'across'. Complete these sentences.

16. Goods being carried from one place to another are in   trans __ __ .

17. Something which lasts or stays for only a short time is said to be   trans __ __ __ __ .

18. Something through which light is shining is   trans __ __ __ __ __ __ .

19. To negotiate or deal is to   trans __ __ __ .

20. If you carry something from one place to another you trans __ __ __ __   it.

Write a colour after each of these words. e.g. sky-blue.

21. nut- _____

22. pitch- _____

23. slate- _____

24. blood- _____

25. bottle- _____

Briefly describe these words.

26. gatehouse _____

27. gatekeeper _____

MARK
✓ or ✗

Briefly describe these words.

28. gatecrasher _____ ☐
29. gatepost _____ ☐
30. gate-money _____ ☐

Write each of these phrases next to its correct meaning

just what the doctor ordered, one's better half, at a loose end,
to do the dirty on, at loggerheads

31. one's spouse _____ ☐
32. to play a low trick _____ ☐
33. exactly what is required _____ ☐
34. quarrelling _____ ☐
35. having nothing to do _____ ☐

Write down the meaning of each of these abbreviations.

36. BBBC _____ ☐
37. VCR _____ ☐
38. BUPA _____ ☐
39. CD _____ ☐
40. d.o.b. _____ ☐

Write out the plurals of these phrases.

41. the governess's philosophy _____ ☐
42. the jumbo's capacity _____ ☐
43. the physician's diagnosis _____ ☐
44. the medicine man's prognosis _____ ☐
45. the druggist's dispensary _____ ☐

Underline the odd one out.

46. scaffold gibbet guillotine cuspidor gallows ☐
47. valley delta glen cwm coomb ghyll ☐
48. dirk caber sporran kilt kookaburra ☐
49. Anastasia Sîan Isaac Yvonne Odette Rowena ☐
50. lucid fatuous stupid ridiculous silly ☐

Complete these definitions.

51. A lepidopterist is a student of _____ and _____ . ☐
52. Halitosis is another name for _____ . ☐
53. If you are recumbent, you are _____ down. ☐
54. A synopsis of a book is a _____ of it. ☐
55. A linchpin is a pin used to keep a _____ on its _____ . ☐

MARK
✓ or ✗

In each sentence write an appropriate NOUN formed from the word in capitals.	56.	IMMOBILE The car was in a state of _____ after the accident.
	57.	MANDATE The instructions are _____ and must be obeyed.
	58.	MINOR Only a _____ of people work at night.
	59.	POTENT James has great _____ as a teacher.
	60.	DELICATE I was impressed by the _____ of the needlework.

Rewrite these sentences, changing to the past tense.	61.	Clint drives the cattle to the river and they swim across. _____
	62.	The joiner comes and does what is needed to be done. _____
	63.	She shakes her head as she rides the dilapidated bicycle. _____
	64.	I will write to my friend when I get home. _____
	65.	He knows as he sings and rings the bell that people hate the noise he makes. _____ _____

Underline the word on the right which belongs with the three on the left.	66.	flag, wane, ebb,	bunting, lessen, flow
	67.	blind, curtain, sash	shutter, cummerbund, door
	68.	janitor, caretaker, attendant	curate, curare, curator
	69.	perplex, mystify, puzzle	flummox, worry, perpetrate
	70.	daily, everyday, commonplace	quota, quondam, quotidian

Put each of these words into its correct sentence.		vapid, incessant, nefarious, tureen, trimaran
	71.	The _____ villain was sentenced to hang on the gallows.
	72.	The silver _____ stood in the centre of the table.
	73.	His new _____ cut effortlessly through the ocean.
	74.	Mrs Hayward possessed a _____ personality and unfortunately had few friends.
	75.	The _____ noise made many millworkers deaf.

Write down one word which describes all in each line.	76.	ream quarto quire foolscap A4 _____
	77.	incisor molar canine fang wisdom _____
	78.	Avon Cornwall Gwent Warwickshire _____
	79.	Centigrade Beaufort Fahrenheit Richter _____
	80.	Eton Harrow Downside Rugby _____

MARK
✓ or ✗

Join these sentences together. Begin with the word 'When' and use a comma.

81. Ruth saw her husband. She ran forward to greet him.

_____ ☐

82. I heard the crash. I rushed to see what had happened.

_____ ☐

83. The milkman knocked at the door. He asked for his money.

_____ ☐

84. Martha saw the cottage. She liked it very much.

_____ ☐

85. The train arrived. Ahmar saw that it was empty.

_____ ☐

Write down the names of the birds which have these peculiar group terms applied to them.

owls,   swans,   crows,   eagles,   starlings

86. a murder of _____ ☐

87. a convocation of _____ ☐

88. a murmuration of _____ ☐

89. a parliament of _____ ☐

90. a herd, bevy, bank, wedge, game, squadron or whiteness of

_____ ☐

General knowledge. Supply the missing information

91. Hieroglyphics was an ancient method of writing, using

_____ . ☐

92. What or who is a tycoon? _____ ☐

93. Who wears a mitre and carries a crosier? _____ , ☐

94. Complete this simile: as _____ as Croesus. ☐

95. If something is pukka (or pucka) it is _____ . ☐

Rewrite and punctuate these sentences.

96. excuse me whispered the old lady may i please pass

_____ ☐

97. i cant get through the old lady muttered

_____ ☐

98. the old lady said that she could not get past

_____ ☐

99. i cant barked the old lady get past

_____ ☐

100. shift roared the old lady

_____ ☐

MARK
✓ or ✗

Write down just one word for each of the phrases in brackets in each of these sentences.	1.	That vehicle is (able to move on land or water). _____
	2.	The (man whose wife has died) is very lonely. _____
	3.	The house is (neglected, abandoned and falling into ruin). _____
	4.	I am afraid that we are in the grip of an (illness that attacks great numbers of people in one place at the same time). _____
	5.	In this matter I am (taking no part on either side). _____

Write an ADJECTIVE from the list next to an appropriate noun.		Stygian, Draconian, Brobdingnagian, labyrinthine, Heath Robinson
	6.	_____ invention
	7.	_____ darkness
	8.	_____ laws
	9.	_____ proportions
	10.	_____ maze

Briefly define these phrases.	11.	pearl-diver _____
	12.	pearly king _____
	13.	Pearly Gates _____
	14.	Pearl Harbor _____
	15.	to cast pearls before swine _____ _____

Write down the plurals of these phrases.	16.	the dormouse's difficulty _____
	17.	the apothecary's pharmacy _____
	18.	the army's phalanx _____
	19.	a marvellous phenomenon _____
	20.	Something that lasts for only a short time is an ephemeron and its plural is _____ .

Write each of these occupations next to its proper definition.		haberdasher, pawnbroker, fletcher, barber, tanner
	21.	cuts hair _____
	22.	cures leather _____
	23.	sells ribbons, buttons, thread etc. _____
	24.	makes arrows _____
	25.	lends money on goods left with him or her _____

General knowledge. Complete these sentences.	26.	If something is utopian it is _____
	27.	Pegasus was a _____
	28.	A grapnel is a _____
	29.	Wrath is very great _____
	30.	A conundrum is a _____

MARK
✓ or ✗

Put each of these words into its correct sentence.

euphemism, personage, dehydration, scuttle, epaulette

31. Lost in the desert, he had not had a drink for two days and was suffering from severe _____ . ☐

32. The captain decided to _____ his own ship rather than let it be taken by the enemy. ☐

33. The Mikado appears as a very grand _____ indeed. ☐

34. Her _____ indicated that she was a high-ranking officer. ☐

35. 'To pass away' is a _____ for 'to die'. ☐

Supply the missing inhabitants.

36. A person who lives on the island of Cyprus is a _____ . ☐

37. A native of Paris is a _____ . ☐

38. A person from Manchester is called a _____ . ☐

39. A person from Liverpool is a _____ . ☐

40. A native of Glasgow is called a _____ . ☐

Write one word on each line which has both the meanings given.

41. a colour _____ noise made by a badly-tuned engine ☐

42. a military fête _____ a design on the skin ☐

43. a mixture _____ an enclosed area for living ☐

44. out of uniform, you're in _____ an expert in Islamic law ☐

45. a smart reply _____ a glass laboratory vessel ☐

Complete these definitions.

46. The Plimsoll line was devised to prevent ships being _____ ☐

47. The Decalogue is another name for the _____ ☐

48. A gendarme is a French _____ ☐

49. To run the gauntlet is to undergo severe _____ ☐

50. A kleptomaniac cannot help _____ ☐

Rewrite correctly, putting in all the necessary punctuation.

51-55. that was an interesting excuse said mrs walters with a smile but im afraid i dont believe a word of it henry scowled but said nothing

_____

_____

_____

Number between 0 and 5

☐

MARK
✓ or ✗

The prefix 'fore-' means 'beforehand' or 'in front'. Complete these sentences.	56.	A tuft of hair on the fore _ _ _ _ is a fore _ _ _ _ _ .
	57.	Predicting what is to happen is a fore _ _ _ _ .
	58.	To have an idea that something evil is about to happen is to fore _ _ _ _ .
	59.	A fore _ _ _ _ conclusion is when you are able to tell with certainty what will happen.
	60.	Fore _ _ _ _ _ _ is fore _ _ _ _ _ is a well-known proverb.

Underline the odd one out in each line.	61.	gosling nestling duckling porkling curling
	62.	trivial unimportant momentous trifling paltry
	63.	Wordsworth Beethoven Haydn Brahms Handel
	64.	rickshaw taxi hackney carriage cycle omnibus
	65.	Caledonia Hibernia Anglia Anaemia Cambria

'Fathers'. Complete these sentences.	66.	William Caxton (1422-1491) is known as the Father of English _____ .
	67.	The Venerable Bede (673-735) is known as the Father of English _____ .
	68.	Izaak Walton (1593-1683) is the Father of _____ .
	69.	Geoffrey Chaucer (1340-1400) is the Father of English _____ .
	70.	Hippocrates (c. 460-377 BC) is the Father of _____ .

Here are the first lines of some well-known poems. After each one write down the name of the person who wrote it.	71.	They went to sea in a Sieve, they did _____
	72.	And did those feet in ancient time _____
	73.	I must go down to the seas again, to the lonely sea and the sky, _____
	74.	Macavity's a Mystery Cat: he's called the Hidden Paw − _____
	75.	All winter through I bow my head _____

A simile compares one thing with another. Use your imagination and write an interesting simile to complete each of these sentences.	76.	Contentedly, the baby slept like _____
	77.	The sea pounded against the cliff like _____ _____
	78.	Fallen blossom lay like _____
	79.	I sped down the hill on my bicycle like _____ _____
	80.	The house was as quiet as _____

MARK
✓ or ✗

Join these pairs of sentences together. Begin each new sentence with 'Although' and use a comma.

81. It was after nine o'clock. Paul still dawdled to school.
     _____ ☐

82. Mr Briggs was ninety years old. He walked to town and back every day. _____

     _____ ☐

83. Alice had the flu. She insisted on going to work.
     _____ ☐

84. Jane and Jill were sisters. They did not get on well.
     _____ ☐

85. The rest of the menu looked appetising. Ian still preferred chicken.
     _____

     _____ ☐

Write down the names of these rooms.

86. A room just under the roof is a _____ or an _____ . ☐

87. An artist or a sculptor works in a _____ . ☐

88. A room in a church for storing vestments is a _____ . ☐

89. A large dining-room in a college or monastery is a _____ . ☐

90. The room in which surgical operations are performed is called a
     _____ . ☐

In the brackets write a word which can come before each of the other words in the line.

91. (   ) graduate   natal   script   chaise   mark ☐

92. (   ) mate   out   off   in   point ☐

93. (   ) less   like   benefit   birth   hood ☐

94. (   ) up   bridge   back   out   near ☐

95. (   ) blue   box   breaker   field   pick ☐

A palindrome is a word or phrase which reads the same backwards as forwards, e.g. Madam I'm Adam. Work out these palindromic words from the clues given.

96.   maternal person   _____ keeping quiet ☐
97.   a rotating part   _____ a revolving aerofoil ☐
98.   this brings you round _____ a stimulant ☐
99.   neck and neck in the race _____ horizontal ☐
100. made into a god   _____ treated as a god ☐

(Another famous palindrome is Napoleon's reputed saying: "Able was I ere I saw Elba.")

MARK
✓ or ✗

Here are five very unusual adjectives. Put each one into its most appropriate sentence. Read all five sentences first.

lilliputian, saturnine, Rhadamanthine, philistine, Herculean

1. With _____ strength he pushed the car clear of the injured child.

2. Despite her _____ size she was a tower of strength to everyone who knew her.

3. His _____ face was gloomy and grave.

4. The law was enforced with _____ severity.

5. He has a _____ attitude to life and much prefers plastic and concrete to craftsmanship and style.

Complete these definitions.

6. Velocity is another word for _____ .

7. A wainwright builds or repairs _____ .

8. Another word for dyspepsia is _____ .

9. A carapace is the _____ .

10. If you scrutinise something you examine it _____ .

Briefly describe these phrases.

11. time-consuming _____

12. time capsule _____

13. time machine _____

14. make good time _____

15. time-limit _____

Put each of these words into its correct sentence.

ruminant, reveille, scarlatina, sceptre, yahoo

16. _____ sounds every morning to wake the soldiers up.

17. An animal like a cow, which chews the cud, is a _____ .

18. A _____ is a sign or symbol of kingship.

19. A word meaning scarlet fever is _____ .

20. A brutal or boorish lout is sometimes called a _____ .

In each sentence write down the appropriate room.

21. A woman's private sitting-room or bedroom is a _____ .

22. The central room or court of a Roman house was the _____ .

23. A small room or building added on is an _____ .

24. The small room in a house where food is kept is the _____ .

25. A large room for sleeping in a college or a monastery is called a _____ .

In the brackets write a word which can come before each of the other words in the line.

26. ( ) summer club Ocean ink rope-trick

27. ( ) hold arrest boat keeper martin

28. ( ) hole note stone pad ring

MARK
✓ or ✗

Write a word which can come before each of the other words.	29.	( ) cock pod souper hen green	☐
	30.	( ) silver fire lime sand witted	☐

Work out these anagrams using the clues given.	31.	DEAR SIR	(attackers)	_____ ☐
	32.	BEAR NORTH	(really detestable)	_____ ☐
	33.	VAN TO RIGA	(he'll find a way)	_____ ☐
	34.	WENT MODERN	(great surprise)	_____ ☐
	35.	RESULT	(in Ireland)	_____ ☐

In each sentence write the past participle of the word in capitals.	36.	UNDERGO	I have _____ many hardships to get this far. ☐
	37.	UNDERTAKE	They have _____ to lay down their arms and surrender. ☐
	38.	WAYLAY	Rachel had been _____ by a cruel mugger. ☐
	39.	WITHSTAND	The old church has _____ centuries of bad weather. ☐
	40.	WRING	Stephanie had _____ her hands with grief when told the sad news. ☐

In each sentence write the present tense of the VERB in capitals.	41.	HURRY	Every morning she _____ to school. ☐
	42.	WORRY	That poor mother _____ about her children. ☐
	43.	TARRY	He _____ on the way to the supermarket for he hates going shopping. ☐
	44.	CARRY	David regularly _____ the shopping for his neighbour. ☐
	45.	FERRY	John _____ the people across the river in his boat. ☐

More malapropisms. Underline the words used wrongly and write the correct words beneath them.	46.	There were malodorous sounds coming from the music room.	☐
		_____	
	47.	Mouldy rock flowered down the sides of the corrupting volcano.	☐
		_____	
	48.	The new tables in the science lavatory have tubercular steel legs.	☐
		_____	
	49.	His speech is so poor that he has to receive electrocution lessons.	☐
		_____	
	50.	The chicks were hatched in an incinerator.	☐
		_____	

MARK
✓ or ✗

The prefix 'inter-' means 'between' or 'among'. Complete these sentences.

51. A peacemaker tries to inter _ _ _ _ between two people. ☐
52. An inter _ _ _ between two acts of a play is also called an inter _ _ _ _ . ☐
53. If you stop something getting from one place to another, you inter _ _ _ _ it. ☐
54. Aeroplane flights between Europe and America are called inter _ _ _ _ _ _ _ _ flights. ☐
55. A busybody will often inter _ _ _ _ in other people's business. ☐

Supply one word for each of these phrases.

56. having plenty of room   c_____ ☐
57. the art of stuffing the skins of dead animals   t_____ ☐
58. a person who does not believe in any god   a_____ ☐
59. a minute hole in the skin   p_____ ☐
60. incapable of making a mistake   in_____ ☐

Underline the correct word in the brackets.

61. A word which means 'draft' is (outline, cold, board-game). ☐
62. A word meaning 'festoon' is (adorn, suppurate, anger). ☐
63. The word 'tier' means (hen, crying, layer). ☐
64. A word which means 'hallmark' is (authorisation, sign, assembly). ☐
65. A 'laggard' is a (plumber, dawdler, foreigner). ☐

General knowledge. Answer these questions.

66. A Member of Parliament (MP) is elected by the people for each _____ in the country. ☐
67. What is a male bee called? _____ ☐
68. What is the name given to an iron basket in which fires are lit in the open air? _____ ☐
69. What is the name of the alcoholic drink made from grapes? _____ ☐
70. What is the name given to the wide-brimmed hat worn by Mexicans? _____ ☐

The prefix 'omni-' means 'all'. Complete these sentences.

71. Someone all-powerful is said to be omni _ _ _ _ _ _ _ . ☐
72. Someone all-knowing is said to be omni _ _ _ _ _ _ _ . ☐
73. A creature able to eat both animal and vegetable food is omni _ _ _ _ _ _ . Such a creature is an omni _ _ _ _ . ☐
74. A vehicle to carry all and sundry who wish to travel on it is called an omni _ _ _ . ☐
75. God is said to be everywhere at the same time and is therefore omni _ _ _ _ _ _ _ . ☐

MARK
✓ or ✗

Complete these analogies.

76. Elizabeth is to Philip as Victoria is to _____ .

77. Taoiseach (pronounced 'tea shock') is to the Republic of Ireland as _____ is to Great Britain.

78. Bow is to stern as vanguard is to _____ .

79. Well-heeled is to down-at-heel as _____ is to indigent.

80. Milk is to _____ as beer is to barrel.

Use 'risen', 'rose' or 'raised' in each of these sentences.

81. The shopkeeper has _____ his prices again.

82. The Phoenix _____ from the ashes.

83. Building costs have _____ a lot in the past year.

84. The gentleman bowed and _____ his hat to the lady.

85. The river _____ and overflowed into the adjacent fields.

Put each of these receptacles into its correct sentence.

decanter, vase, punnet, scuttle, cruet

86. Anna picked flowers from the garden and arranged them in a

_____ .

87. Sita bought a _____ of strawberries from the fruiterer.

88. He poured himself a whisky from the cut-glass _____ .

89. The _____ is empty and needs more salt putting in it.

90. The coal- _____ stood by the fireside.

In each sentence write a NOUN formed from the word in capitals.

91. COMPOSE   She recovered her _____ after the shock.

92. LEGAL   The lawyer questioned the _____ of the document.

93. FORETHINK   _____ could have prevented that accident.

94. DECOROUS   A Victorian lady was expected to behave with modesty and _____ .

95. TENACIOUS   He pursued his career with dogged _____ .

Put each of these popular sayings next to its correct meaning.

to go at it hammer and tongs, to burn one's boats,
to wear one's heart on one's sleeve, to laugh up one's sleeve,
to tilt at windmills

96. to be quietly amused _____

97. fighting imaginary enemies _____

98. to have gone too far to retreat _____

99. with great noise and vigour _____

100. to show one's feelings openly _____

MARK
✓ or ✗

Complete these definitions.

1. A machine for generating electricity is called a   d_____ . ☐

2. A creature with eight tentacles is an _____ . ☐

3. An instrument which indicates atmospheric pressure to show what sort of weather is coming is called a _____ . ☐

4. A person who grinds corn to make flour is a _____ . ☐

5. A vicar or priest preaches from a _____ in church. ☐

More malapropisms. Underline the words used wrongly and write the correct words beneath them.

6. All doctors must take the hypocritical oath before they practise.
_____ ☐

7. The diseased millionaire left all his money to charity.
_____ ☐

8. We're having new Phoenician blinds fitted to the kitchen window.
_____ ☐

9. Pass me the fire distinguisher and I'll put out that small blaze.
_____ ☐

10. The Leader of the Conservatory Party addressed the House.
_____ ☐

The prefix 'mis-' means 'wrong' or 'ill'. Complete these sentences.

11. Someone who hates people is a   mis _ _ _ _ _ _ _ _ _ _ _ . ☐

12. When somebody has wrongly been punished by the law, there has been a   mis _ _ _ _ _ _ _ _ _ of justice. ☐

13. When a child behaves in a naughty fashion he or she is said to be mis _ _ _ _ _ _ _ _ . ☐

14. An error is also known as a   mis _ _ _ _ _ . ☐

15. If you don't say a word properly you
mis _ _ _ _ _ _ _ _ _ it. ☐

Briefly describe these words or phrases.

16. neither fish, flesh nor fowl _____ ☐

17. a fish out of water _____ ☐

18. fishmonger _____ ☐

19. a pretty kettle of fish _____ ☐

20. fish-plate _____ ☐

Underline the correct word in the brackets.

21. If something is obsolete it is (outmoded, outside, novel). ☐

22. If a job is a sinecure it is (easy, poorly paid, difficult). ☐

23. When scouts have a jamboree they have a (kangaroo, festival, sandwich). ☐

24. Grapes are grown in a (vineyard, orchard, grapnel). ☐

25. A rivet is a (hedge, bird, bolt). ☐

MARK
✓ or ✗

Write down a suitable word next to each group term.

actors, corn, fire, hay, eggs

26. a bale of _____ ☐

27. a hail of _____ ☐

28. a clutch of _____ ☐

29. a sheaf of _____ ☐

30. a company of _____ ☐

Put each of these receptacles into its correct sentence.

creel, quiver, sheath, kitbag, scabbard

31. The archer reached for an arrow from his _____ . ☐

32. When he went fishing he carried his catch in a _____ . ☐

33. The soldier carried his spare clothes and personal items in a large _____ over his shoulder. ☐

34. The knight replaced his sword in its _____ . ☐

35. The sharp knife was kept in a leather _____ . ☐

Rewrite this sentence, putting in the necessary punctuation.

36-40. wed better go chris muttered or hell dock an hours wages

_____

_____

_____

Number between 0 and 5

☐

Use a word formed from FLY, FLOW or FLEE in these sentences.

41. The refugees are _____ from the war. ☐

42. The river has _____ through the valley for centuries. ☐

43. The owl _____ across the evening sky. ☐

44. The boys had _____ in terror from the ghostly apparition. ☐

45. The pigeon had _____ for many kilometres to its loft. ☐

Write each of these popular sayings next to its correct meaning.

by hook or by crook, to be sitting pretty, to be on tenterhooks,
to roll out the red carpet, to tip somebody the wink

46. to make somebody very welcome _____ ☐

47. to forewarn somebody _____ ☐

48. in a state of great suspense _____ ☐

49. to be well-off _____ ☐

50. by whatever means necessary _____ ☐

Underline the odd one out in each line.

51. welcome exile banish deport expel ☐

52. intimidate tend bully coerce browbeat ☐

53. uproarious hilarious comical farcical soporific ☐

MARK
✓ or ✗

	54.	sunrise dusk cock crow daybreak dawn |☐
	55.	deny confess admit reveal unburden divulge |☐

Complete these well-known pairs.

56. bubble and _____ ☐
57. Romulus and _____ ☐
58. Darby and _____ ☐
59. Romeo and _____ ☐
60. Hengist and _____ ☐

In each sentence write a NOUN formed from the word in capitals.

61. INGENIOUS The judges were impressed by the _____ of her invention. ☐

62. DRUDGE The poor neglected woman lived a life of _____ . ☐

63. MIME Paul's _____ of his teacher made us all laugh. ☐

64. ANTAGONIST I cannot understand the reason for his _____ towards me. ☐

65. PREFER I have a _____ for cola rather than lemonade. ☐

These are the first lines of some well-known poems. At the end of each line write down the name of the poet.

66. What is this life if, full of care, _____ ☐
67. When fishes flew and forests walked _____ ☐
68. If you can keep your head when all about you _____ ☐
69. ''You are old, Father William,'' the young man said, _____ _____ ☐
70. Half a league, half a league, _____ ☐

Unscramble these anagrams using the clues given.

71. LISTEN (quiet) _____ ☐
72. ROYS MARE (two words: ship from the depths) _____ ☐
73. CURL ADA (a count who enjoyed gore) _____ ☐
74. PACK MEAN TOIL (steals a lot) _____ ☐
75. FLIT ON CHEERING ANGEL (two words: a famous caring person) _____ ☐

Write down one (or two) word(s) which describe(s) all on each line.

76. Bader Richthofen Bleriot Cheshire _____ ☐
77. mashie niblick driver wedge _____ ☐
78. Colorado Oklahoma Oregon Nebraska Utah _____ ☐

MARK
✓ or ✗

Write down one word which describes all on each line.	79.	Constable Gainsborough Van Gogh Whistler _____
	80.	chamois dik-dik kudu impala springbok _____

Put each of these words into its correct sentence.		envelop, envelope, formally, formerly, latterly
	81.	Earlier in the year he was quite poorly but _____ he has shown signs of improvement.
	82.	Grandmother tends to _____ me in her arms whenever she sees me.
	83.	Mrs Wilson came across to us and _____ introduced herself.
	84.	Although he is now a teacher, _____ he was a miner.
	85.	I hurriedly pushed the letter back into its _____ .

Write down what might be the most appropriate 'opposite' to each of these words.	86.	speaker _____
	87.	lawyer _____
	88.	author _____
	89.	hound _____
	90.	king or queen _____

In each sentence write an ADJECTIVE formed from the word in capitals.	91.	CUSTODY Your crime was so serious," said the judge, "that I must impose a _____ sentence."
	92.	FORTY We held a big party for Dad's _____ birthday.
	93.	FLAME This material is _____ and should be kept well away from fire.
	94.	LEARN The university professor was a very _____ person.
	95.	SATISFY I hope we can bring matters to a _____ conclusion.

Write an interesting simile in each of these sentences.	96.	Like a _____ , the robber approached the house.
	97.	As _____ , the runner approached the finishing tape.
	98.	Like _____ , the angry tigress attacked.
	99.	Like _____ , lightning flashed across the sky.
	100.	Like _____ , the early morning sun rose in the azure sky.